To: Milly Wade Hunter and
Levi
From Wanda and N.E. 1903

The "Reel" Thing

a story of hope and joy

The "catch of the day" is hope!!
Hunter D. Darden

written by Hunter D. Darden

illustrated by Nicole Arnold

Much joy always,
Nicole Arnold

Darden, Hunter D.
The Reel Thing by Hunter D. Darden
Illustrations by Nicole Arnold

To Steve
            —N.A.

All illustrations in this book were done in Prismacolor colored pencils on
Strathmore bristol board 500 series 2-ply white paper.

Summary: a story of hope, joy and friendship
Title: Easy

Library of Congress Catalog Number 2001 126046
ISBN Number 0-9653729-3-6

First Printing 2002

Printed and bound in South Korea through Pacifica Communications

Published by Sunfleur Publications, Inc.

I dedicate this book to my son, Tyler, whose joyful exuberance touches the lives of everyone who has the pleasure of knowing him.

"Today's the day I'm going to catch Madame Mossback!" Charlie said excitedly as he dressed for another day of fishing. Everyone in town had given up hope years before of ever catching "The Madame"…that is… all except for Charlie.

Charlie took the quickest route to the kitchen. His mom was busy making his favorite breakfast over the screaming sounds of his hungry little sister.

Charlie said to his Mom, "Today's the day I'm going to catch Madame Mossback!"
"Sure you will, Charlie," said his mother as she smiled to herself.
"You should come join me at the fishing pond. You could use a break," said Charlie.

Charlie's mom wished him luck as he raced out the door. Feeling more refreshed, she realized that Charlie's excited spirit had spread to her as well. Childhood memories of trying to catch "The Madame" swirled in her mind.

Charlie spotted the paperboy on his delivery route.
"Hey Tyler!" he yelled excitedly. "Today's the day I'm going to catch Madame Mossback!"
Tyler said, "Good luck! Maybe I'll grab a pole and try my luck, too."

"Hey, Mr. Smith!" Charlie hollered at the mailman as he passed him.
"Today's the day I'm going to catch Madame Mossback!"
"Sure you will, Charlie," said Mr. Smith smiling, recalling his
excitement many years before from trying to catch "The Madame."
'Where had those fun days gone anyway?' he thought to himself.

Charlie always dropped by every summer morning to say hello to his grandmother.
He knew she would be watering her flowers as she did every morning.
"Hey, Nana! Today's the day I'm going to catch Madame Mossback!" Charlie yelled.
Seeing Charlie's happy face reminded her of Granddad's and her many attempts at
trying to catch "The Madame."

Charlie spotted his Dad's friend, Mr. Harris, rushing to a business meeting as usual.
"Hey, Mr. Harris! Today's the day I'm going to catch Madame Mossback!" Charlie exclaimed.
"Good luck!" said Mr. Harris as he thought to himself, 'Why am I rushing around like this when I could use a day of fishing, too?'

Charlie stopped off at The Fishing Line to pick up his special bait.
"Hey, Mr. Kishimoto. Today's the day I'm going to catch Madame Mossback!"
"Sure you will, Charlie," said Mr. Kishimoto as he thought to himself, 'I just
might have to close early today and do a little fishing myself.'

As Charlie arrived at the fishing hole, he noticed the new boy from school fishing all by himself.

Charlie said, "Hey, my name is Charlie. Today's the day I'm going to catch Madame Mossback!"

The boy said, "My name is Juan. Who's Madame Mossback?"

"She's just the oldest and biggest bass in the lake. She's been around so long that moss grows on her back."

Juan said, "Today's the day we're going to catch Madame Mossback. Let's get started!"

Charlie and Juan threw their lines in the water and waited…and waited…

no bite…

no nibble…

no Madame Mossback…

(Can you spot her?)

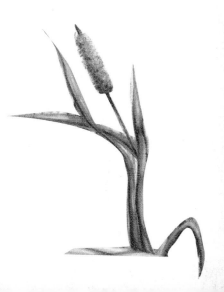

Soon Tyler came down to join in on the fun after finishing his paper route.
Charlie, Juan and Tyler threw their lines in the water and waited…and waited…

no bite…

no nibble…

no Madame Mossback…

(Look carefully and I bet you can find her.)

Mr. Smith, the mailman, came along to try his luck, too. Charlie, Juan, Tyler and Mr. Smith threw their lines in the water and waited…and waited…

no bite…

no nibble…

no Madame Mossback…

(Do you see her now?)

Mr. Harris, the businessman, was the next person to appear at the fishing hole to join in on the fun. Charlie, Juan, Tyler, Mr. Smith and Mr. Harris threw their lines in the water and waited…and waited…

no bite…

no nibble…

no Madame Mossback…

(Are you still looking for her?)

After closing the bait shop a little early, Mr. Kishimoto came to try his luck. Charlie, Juan, Tyler, Mr. Smith, Mr. Harris and Mr. Kishimoto threw their lines in the water and waited…and waited…

no bite…

no nibble…

no Madame Mossback…

(Did you catch a glimpse?)

Charlie's mother and grandmother appeared with a picnic basket of food for the fishing friends. Charlie, Juan, Tyler, Mr. Smith, Mr. Harris, Mr. Kishimoto, Mom and Nana threw their lines in the water and waited…and waited…

no bite…

no nibble…

no Madame Mossback…

(Where is she now?)

As the group of new friends was walking through the field away from the fishing hole Charlie shouted out, "Don't forget! Tomorrow's the day we're going to catch Madame Mossback!"

Lift and Turn

Just then, Madame Mossback jumped out of the water to say, "They may not have caught me, but they caught something much more important… friendship. They learned that the joy of "catching" good friends and the pleasure that is spread from a happy attitude are the real "reel" things".